TWELVE EASY PIECES FOR FLUTE WITH PIANO ACCOMPANIMENT

I Can't Believe Pieces Can Be This Easy!

PAUL HARRIS

CHESTER MUSIC
8/9 Frith Street, London, W1D 3JB

Exclusive distributors:
Chester Music
(A division of Music Sales Limited)
8/9 Frith Street, London W1D 3JB, England.

Music Sales Corporation
257 Park Avenue South, New York, NY 10010,
United States of America.

Music Sales Pty Limited
120 Rothschild Avenue, Rosebery, NSW 2018, Australia.

Order No. CH64999
ISBN 0-7119-9498-6

Music Processed by Andrew Shiels
Cover design by Chloë Alexander
Printed in Great Britain

www.musicsales.com

Contents

1 First Flute

to Philip Mundey

Allegretto con moto

2 With Fife and Plum

12
12

16
p
f
16

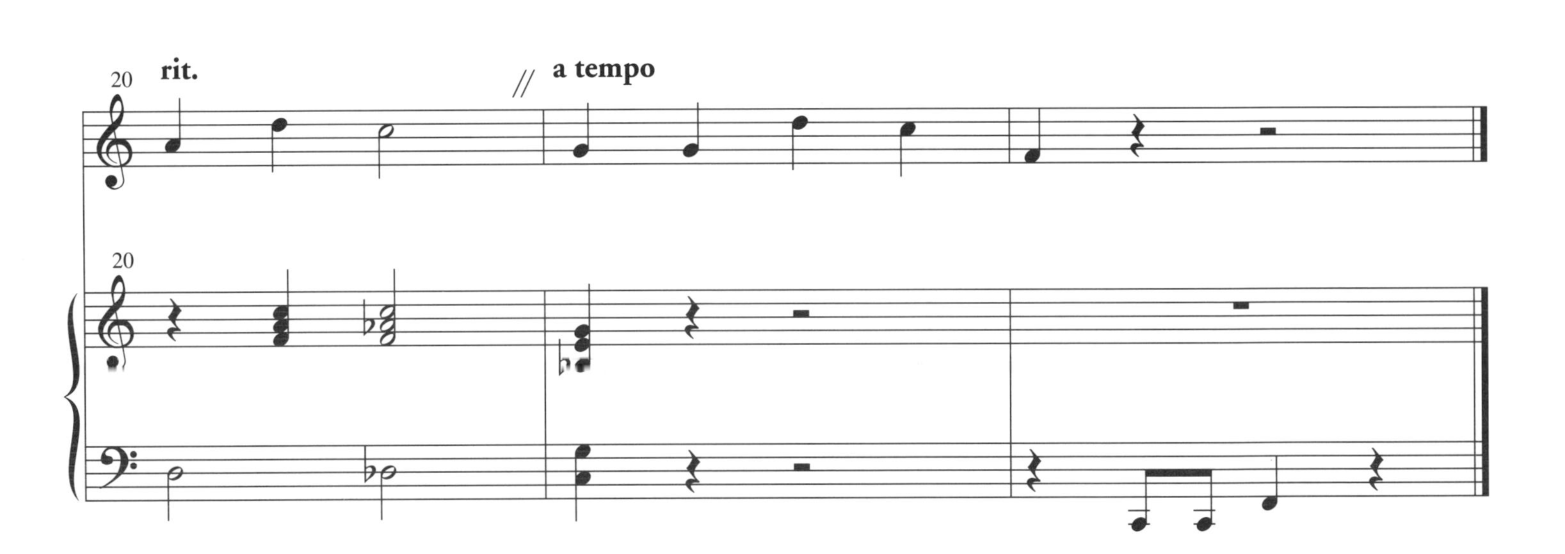
20
rit.
a tempo
20

3 Funky Foot-joint

10
10
14
p
14
p
17
f
17
f
20
20

4 My First CD

f

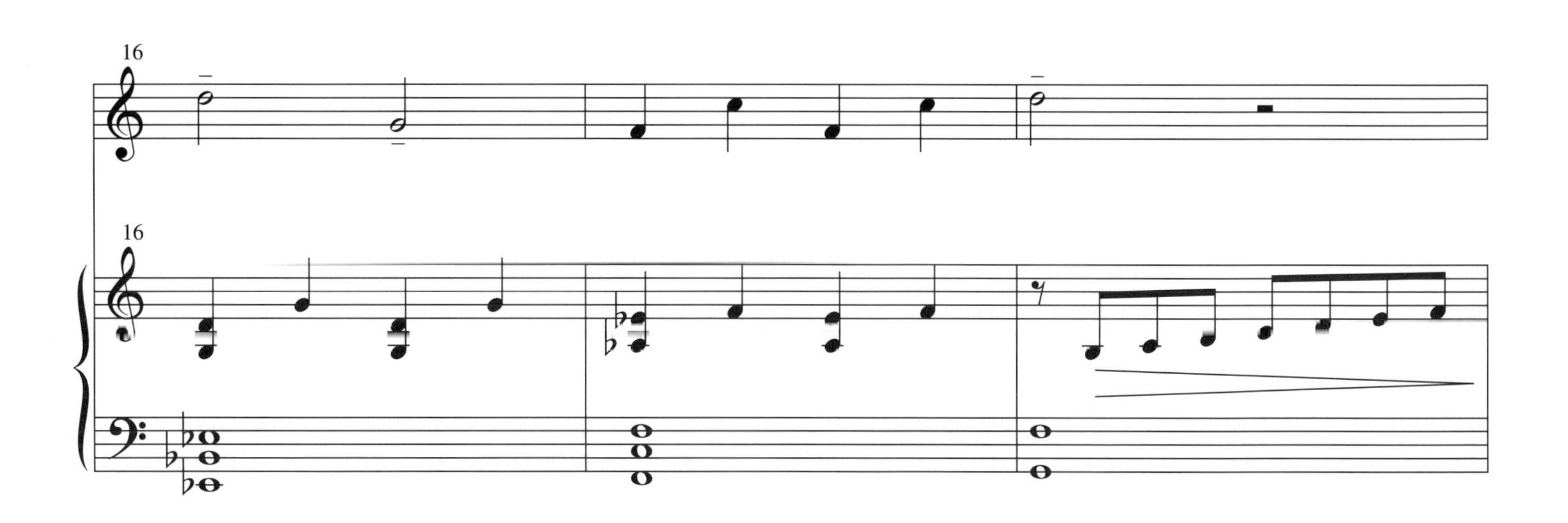

19
p

22
f
mf

25
Ped.

5 Flute Salad

11
11
mp
15
p
15
p
18
18
21
f
21
f

6 I Sat On My Flute

to Graham de vere White

10
10
13
f
13
f
Ped.
16
16
19
p
19

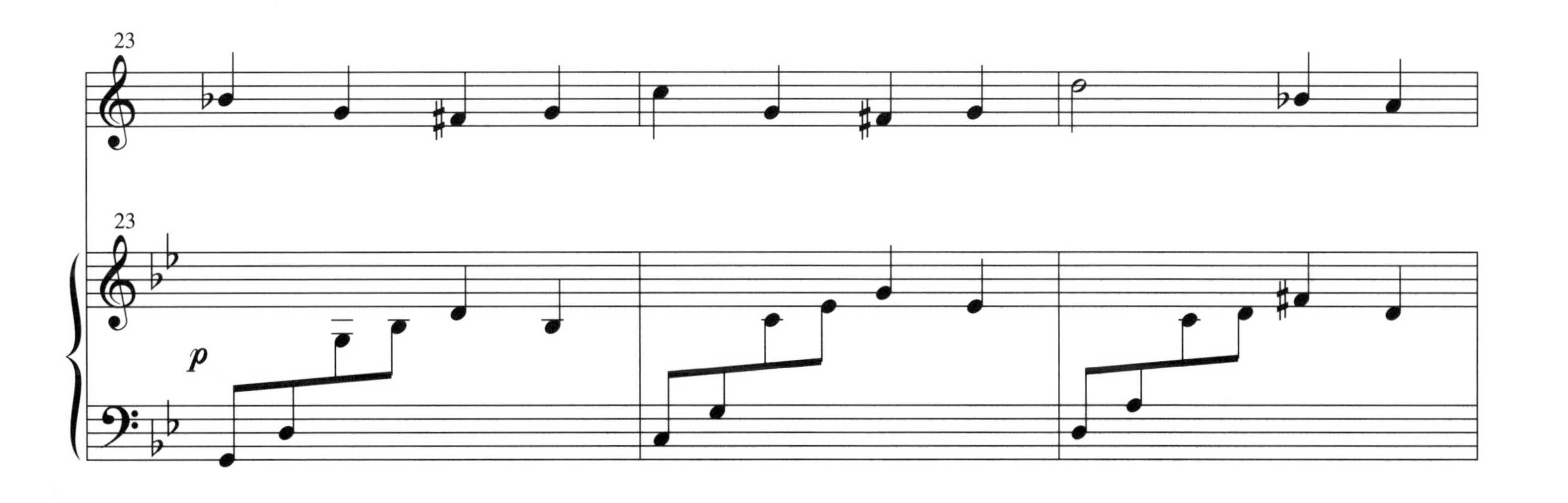
23
23
p

26
26

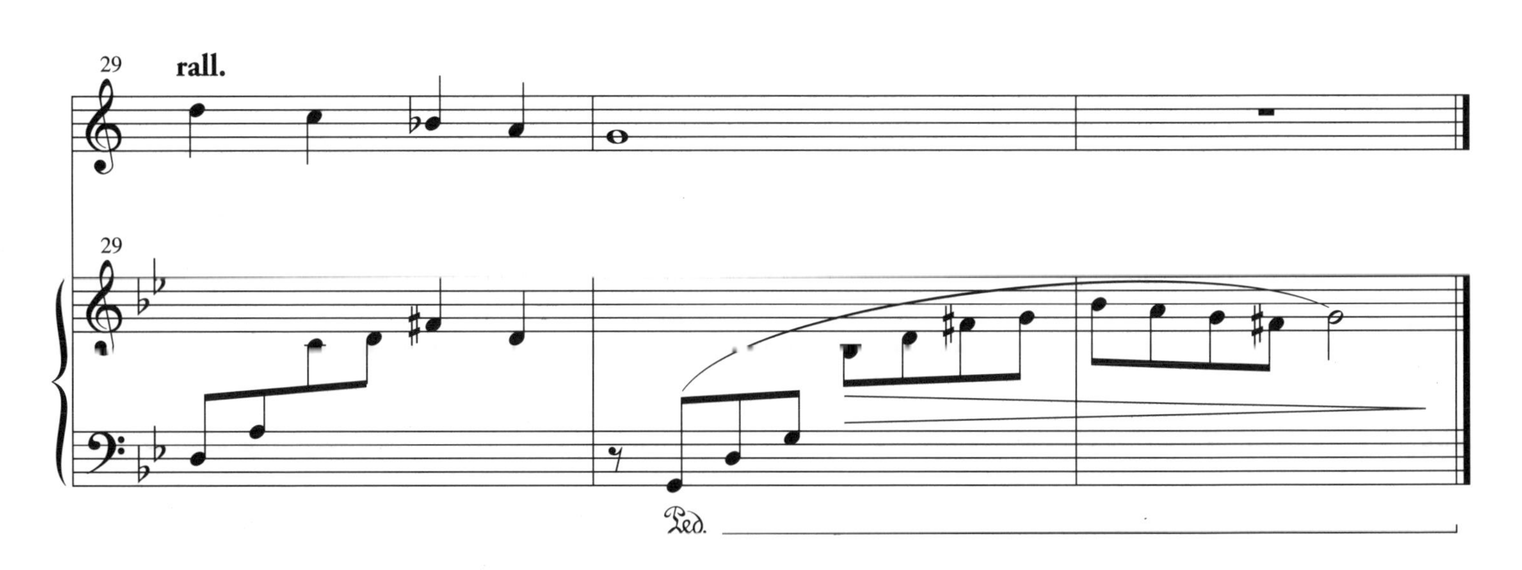
29
rall.
29
Ped.

7 Chinese Flute Tea

14
p
14
p
18
f
18
f
22
p
22
p
26
f
26
f

8 Head-joint Blues

10
f
f
13
16
3
19

9 Sonata in C ('The Great') Op.547b no.38

to Sally

10
f
10
f
14
poco rit.
14
17
a tempo
17
21
21

10 I Wish I Practised More!

11
f
11
mf
14
14
18
18
21
21

11 The Silver Flute

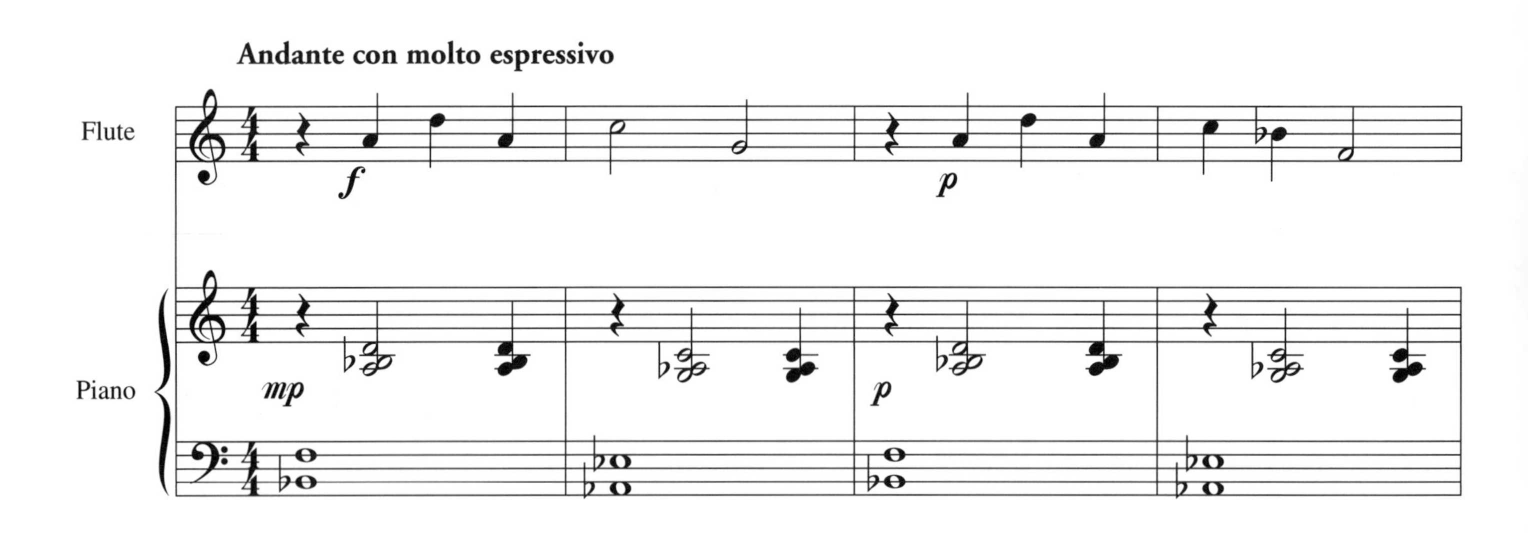

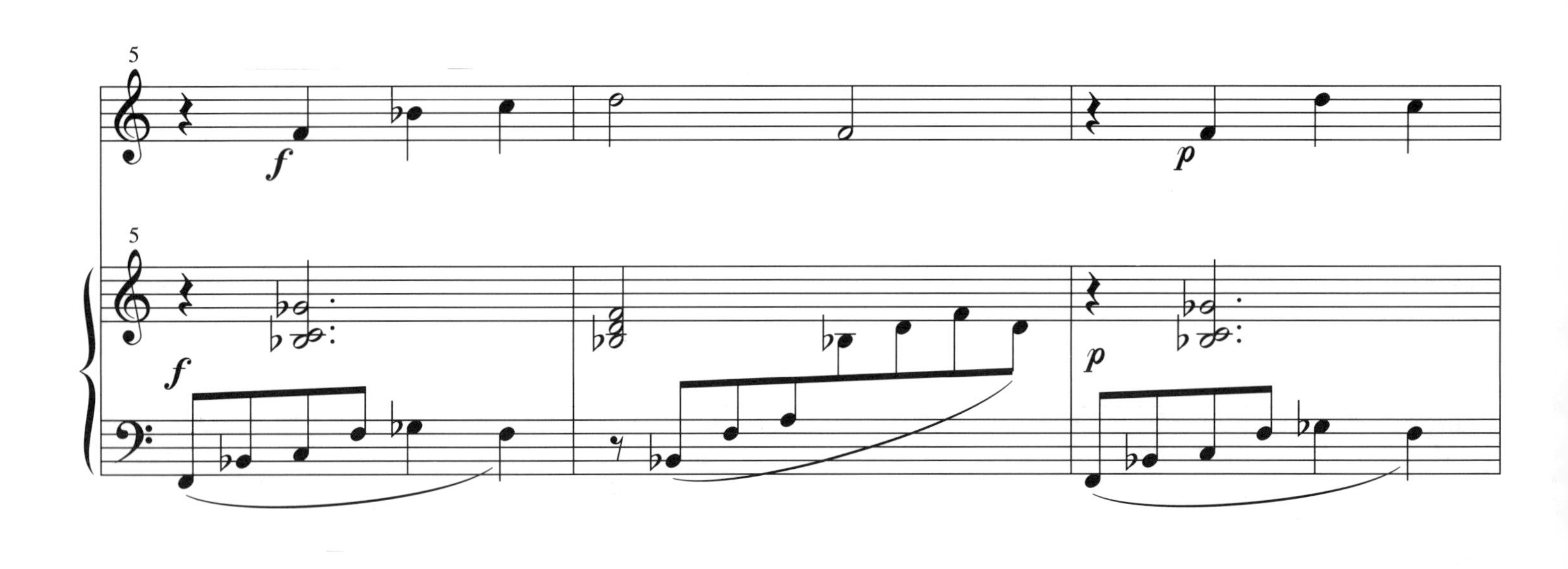

11
11
15
15
19
19
p
f
p
f
23
rit.
p
23
p
Ped.

12 Latin Lip-plate

10
p
10
p

13
f
13
f

16
16

19
19

22
22

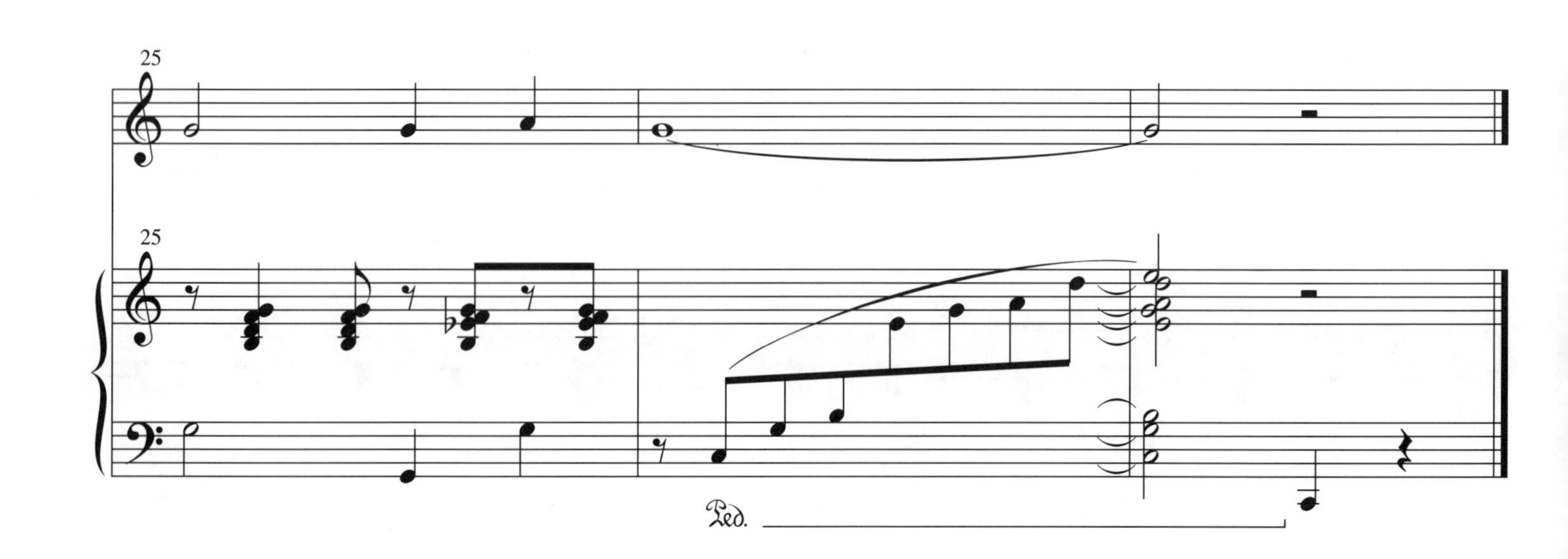
25
25
Ped.

Also by Paul Harris...

CLOWNS

A unique collection of seven original pieces for Flute and Piano
aimed at Grade II - III players.

1. **Scapino**
2. **Pierrot**
3. **Pulcinella**
4. **Columbine**
5. **Harlequin**
6. **Pantalon**
7. **Scaramouche**